KEYBOARD GAMES

By Marilyn Lowe
In Cooperation With Edwin E. Gordon

Music Moves for Piano is designed to develop improvisation, audiation, and keyboard performance skills. The method builds on the ideas and theories of Orff, Kodaly, Dalcroze, Suzuki, and Gordon.

G-7217
© 2007, 2008, 2011, 2015 Music Moves LLC
www.musicmovesforpiano.com
info@musicmovesforpiano.com
ISBN: 978-1-57999-699-4

Distributed by GIA Publications, Inc.
7404 S. Mason Ave., Chicago, IL 60638
(708) 496-3800 or (800) 442-1358
www.giamusic.com

Printed in the United States of America

February 2017

Table of Contents

Symbols Used for Beginning Performance Pieces

Fingers/Hands

S^1 Starting finger (starts the piece)

S^2 Starting finger of the other hand

Play these fingers at the same time

Piano Keys

S^1 Starting key (starts the piece)

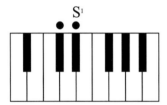

S^2 Starting key for the other hand

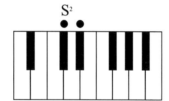

Play these keys at the same time

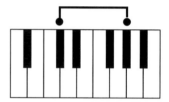

Arrows/Recording

Arrows show the direction to play

Home Study CD

Keyboard Playing Location

Black dots show the keyboard playing location. Black dots are **on** the white keys. Black dots are **above** the black keys.

Chocolate Chip Cookies

Track 1

Use the LH middle finger throughout.

Student

Duet

RH = upstems LH = downstems

Rhythm Pattern Chant
Du-de Du Du-de Du
Du-de Du Du Du

A little soft
Not too slow

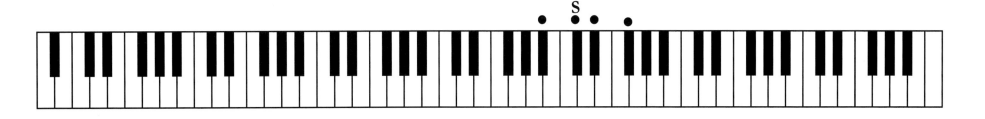

The Big Black Bear

Use the LH middle finger throughout

| Rhythm Pattern Chant
Du-da-di Du-da-di
Du-da-di Du | | Loud
Slow |

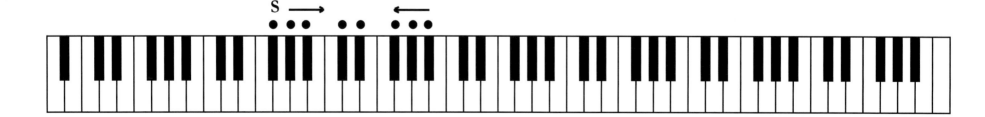

Creepy Crawly

Track 3

Rhythm Pattern Chant
Du-da-di Du-da-di

Soft
Slow

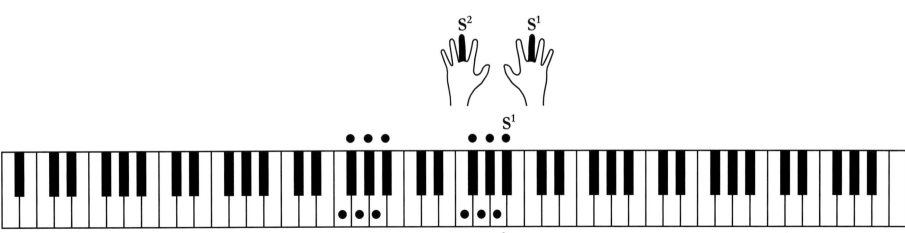

Yankee Doodle

RH = upstems LH = downstems

Rhythm Pattern Chant
Du Du Du Du

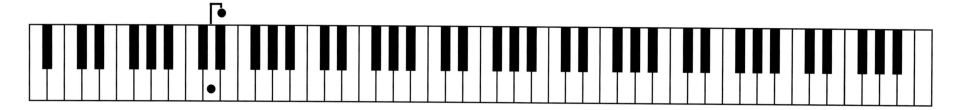

The Flower Garden

RH = upstems LH = downstems

Use the middle fingers throughout

Rhythm Pattern Chant
Du-da-di Du-da-di
Du-da-di Du

Soft
Slow

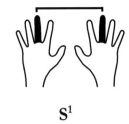

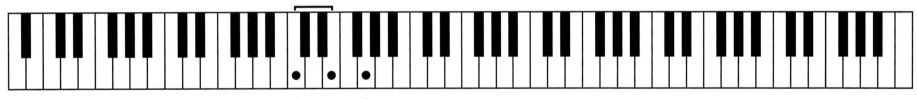

6

Waddling Ducks

Use the middle finger of each hand
RH = upstems LH = downstems

Rhythm Pattern Chant
Du-de Du-de
Du-de Du

Loud
Slow

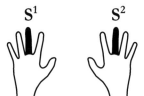

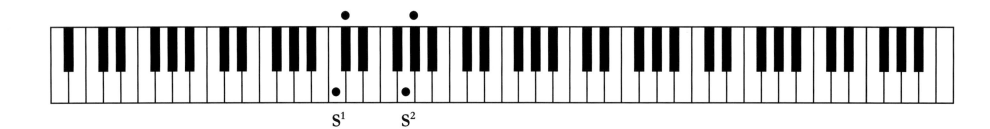

The Parachute. The Diver.

First, play slowly. Second, play fast.
Use the middle finger of the right hand throughout the piece

Track
7

Rhythm Pattern Chant	The Parachute	The Diver
Du-da-di Du-da-di	Loud	Soft
Du-da-di Du	Slow	Fast

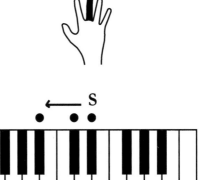

_____

My Story

low	middle	high	loud	soft	fast	slow	Rhythm chant: Du-de Du	Du-da-di Du-da-di

_____

| low | middle | high | loud | soft | fast | slow | Rhythm chant: Du-de Du-de | Du-da-di Du |

_____

| low | middle | high | loud | soft | fast | slow | Rhythm chant: Du-de Du-de | Du-da-di Du-da-di |

_____

| low | middle | high | loud | soft | fast | slow | Rhythm chant: Du-de Du | Du-da-di Du-da-di |

_____

| low | middle | high | loud | soft | fast | slow | Rhythm chant: Du-de Du-de | Du-da-di Du |

_____

| low | middle | high | loud | soft | fast | slow | Rhythm chant: Du-de Du | Du-da-di Du |

_____

INSTRUCTIONS. The teacher-parent writes the student's story on the lines. Circle the choice of performance ideas. Encourage thinking about different levels of soft-loud and slow-fast, such as "not too soft" or "a little fast." The student improvises the music. This creative project may be completed in class or at home. It may be an individual project or a group project.

Pepperoni Macaroni

Track 8

Duet

Student

RH = upstems LH = downstems
Use the middle finger throughout.

**Rhythm Pattern Chant
Du-da-di Du-da-di
Du-da-di Du**

**A little loud
A little fast**

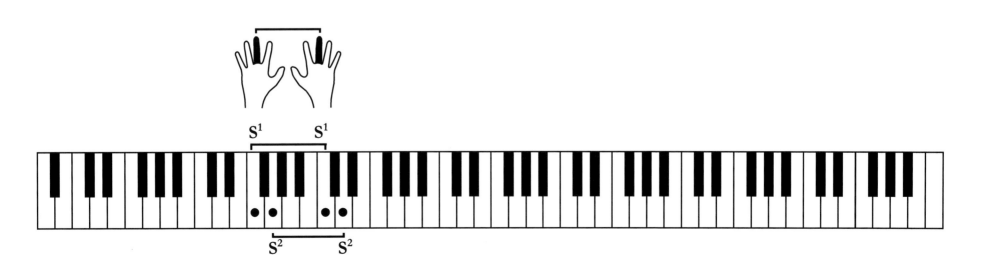

Valentine Box

Track 9

Use the middle finger of either hand
Play one octave higher

Hold the damper pedal down for the whole piece

Rhythm Pattern Chant
Du-de Du-de Du-de Du-de

Soft
Not too slow

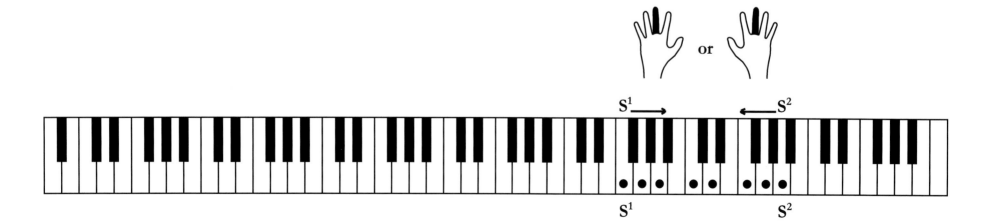

Sinking

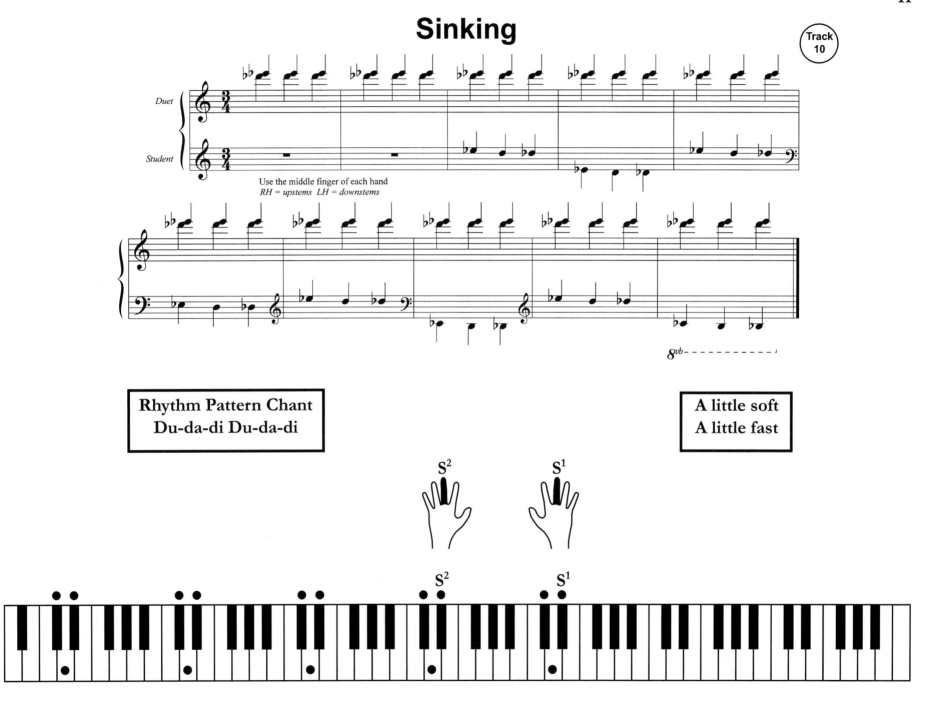

Ring Around the Rosy

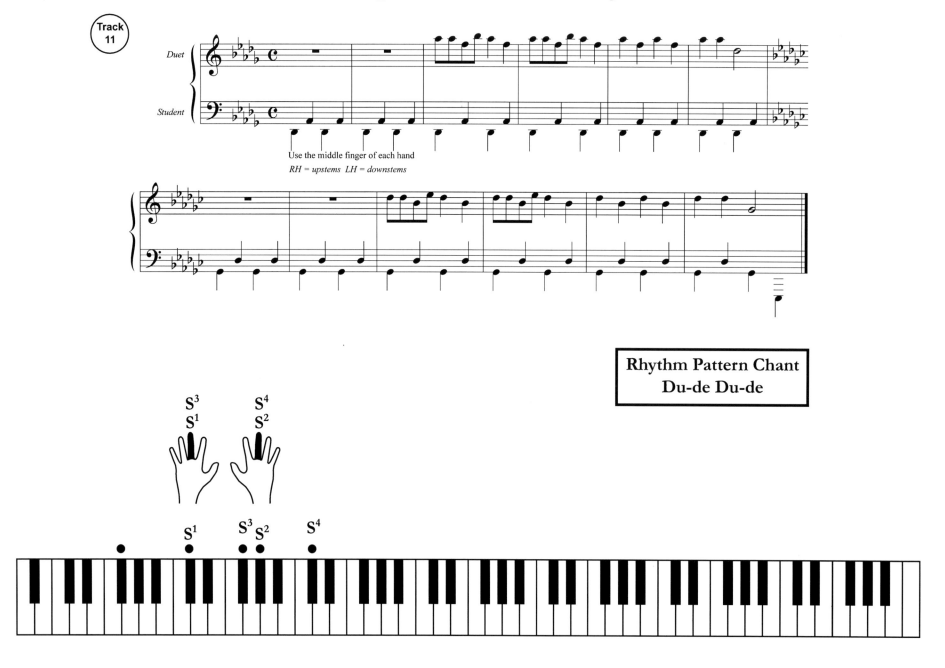

Use the middle finger of each hand
RH = upstems LH = downstems

**Rhythm Pattern Chant
Du-de Du-de**

Dance of the Penguins

RH = upstems LH = downstems

Rhythm Pattern Chant	A little loud
Du-da-di Du-da-di	**Slow**
Du-da-di Du	

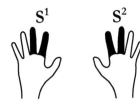

14

_____

My Story

low middle high	loud soft	fast slow	Rhythm chant:	Du-ta-de-ta Du-de	Du-da-di Du
low middle high	loud soft	fast slow	Rhythm chant:	Du-de Du-ta-de-ta	Du-da-di Du-da-di
low middle high	loud soft	fast slow	Rhythm chant:	Du-ta-de-ta Du-de	Du-da-di Du-da-di
low middle high	loud soft	fast slow	Rhythm chant:	Du-de Du-de	Du-da-di Du
low middle high	loud soft	fast slow	Rhythm chant:	Du-de Du	Du-da-di Du-da-di
low middle high	loud soft	fast slow	Rhythm chant:	Du-ta-de-ta Du-de	Du da di Du-da-di

INSTRUCTIONS. The teacher-parent writes the student's story on the lines. Circle the choice of performance ideas. Encourage thinking about different levels of soft-loud and slow-fast, such as "not too soft" or "a little fast." The student improvises the music. This creative project may be completed in class or at home. It may be an individual project or a group project.

Are You Sleeping

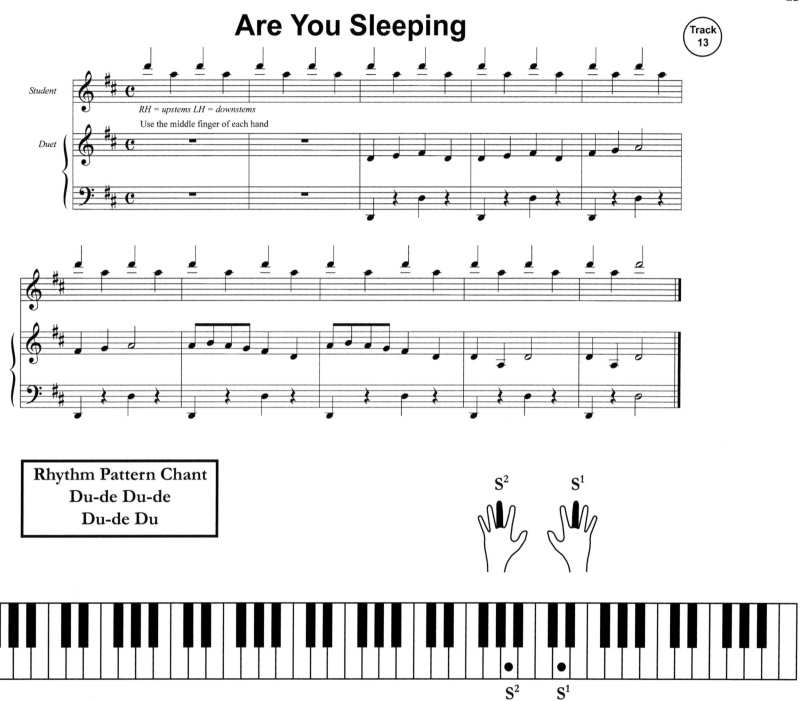

Rhythm Pattern Chant
Du-de Du-de
Du-de Du

The Ghost

S

Track 14

Duet

Student

Use the left hand middle finger

**Rhythm Pattern Chant
Du-de Du-de
Du-de Du**

**Not too soft
Slow**

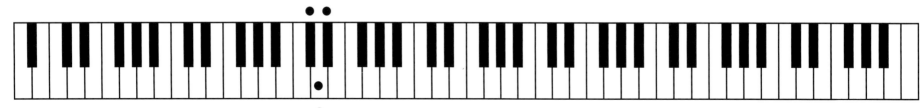

Splashing in Puddles

RH = upstems LH = downstems
Use the middle finger throughout.

Rhythm Pattern Chant
Du-da-di Du-da-di

A little loud
A little slow

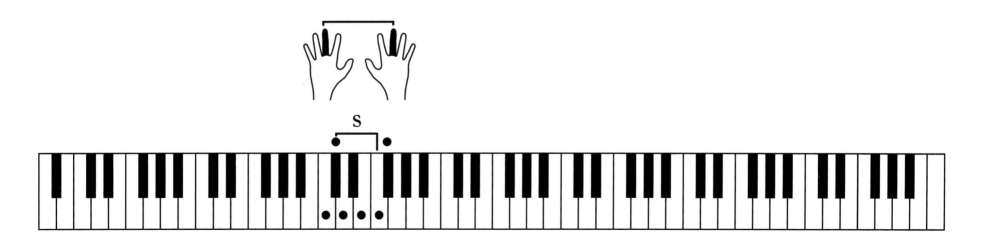

Mary Had a Little Lamb

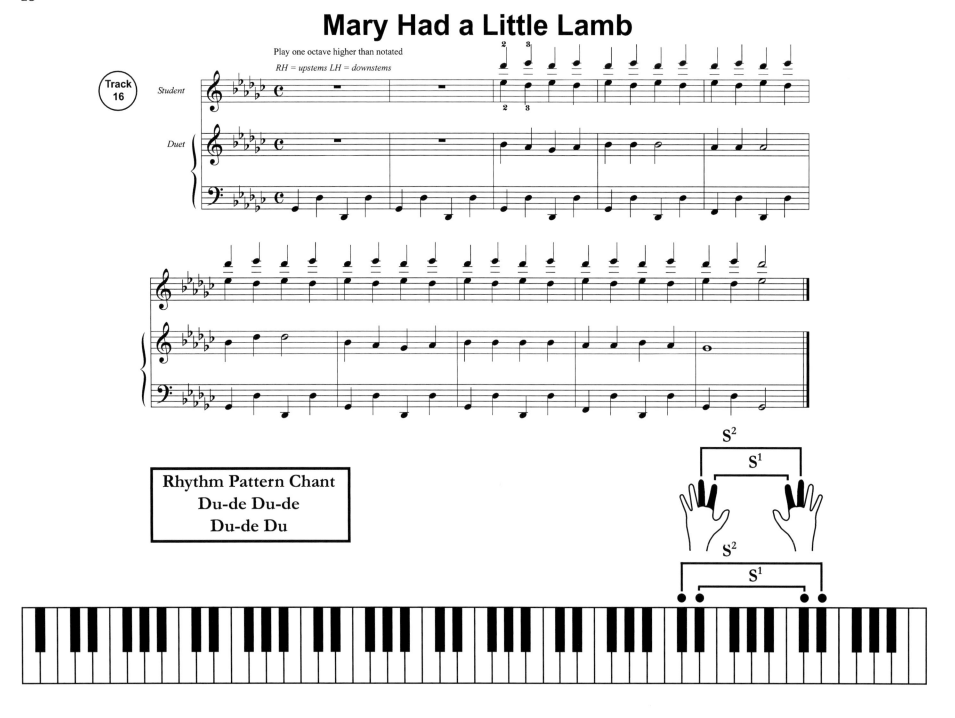

Track 16

Student

Duet

Play one octave higher than notated

RH = upstems LH = downstems

Rhythm Pattern Chant
Du-de Du-de
Du-de Du

Bears' Waltz

Track 17

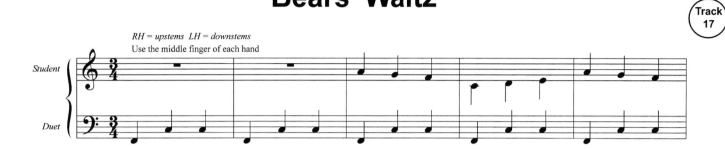

Rhythm Pattern Chant
Du-da-di Du-da-di
Du-da-di Du

A little loud
A little slow

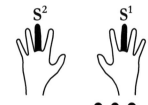

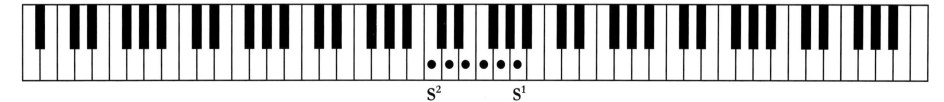

The Jazzy Crocodile

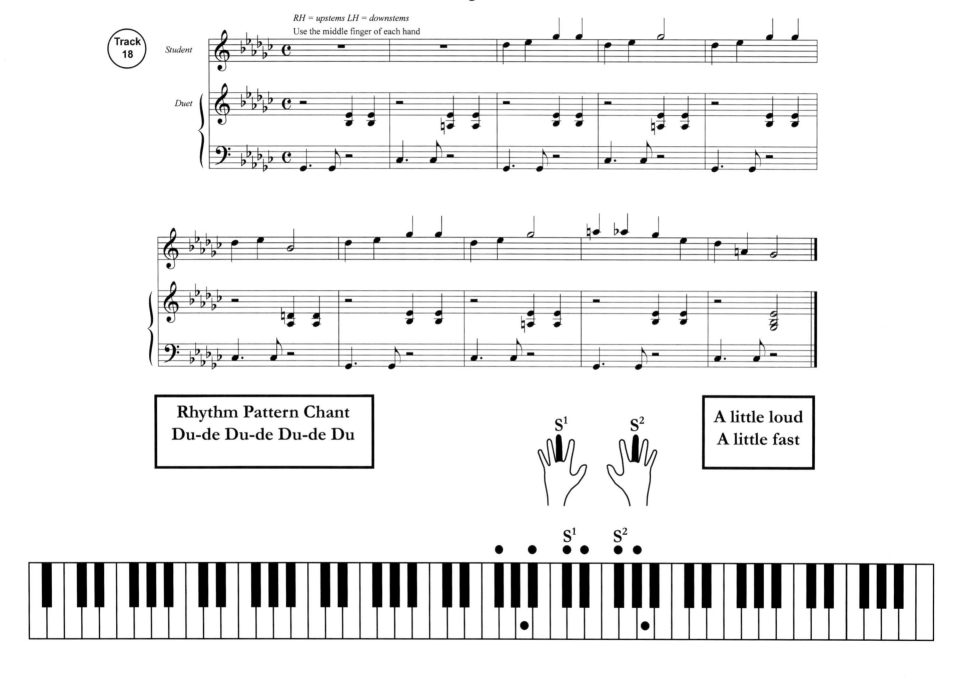

Rhythm Pattern Chant
Du-de Du-de Du-de Du

A little loud
A little fast

My Story

low	middle	high	loud	soft	fast	slow	Rhythm chant:	Du-de Du-ta-de-ta	Du-da-di Du-da-di

low	middle	high	loud	soft	fast	slow	Rhythm chant:	Du-de Du-de	Du-da-di Du-da-di

low	middle	high	loud	soft	fast	slow	Rhythm chant:	Du-ta-de-ta Du-de	Du-da-di Du-da-di

low	middle	high	loud	soft	fast	slow	Rhythm chant:	Du-de Du-de	Du-da-di Du

low	middle	high	loud	soft	fast	slow	Rhythm chant:	Du-ta-de-ta Du	Du-da-di Du-da-di

low	middle	high	loud	soft	fast	slow	Rhythm chant:	Du-de Du	Du-da-di Du-da-di

INSTRUCTIONS. The teacher-parent writes the student's story on the lines. Circle the choice of performance ideas. Encourage thinking about different levels of soft-loud and slow-fast, such as "not too soft" or "a little fast." The student improvises the music. This creative project may be completed in class or at home. It may be an individual project or a group project.

Three Blind Mice

Track 19

Play both hands one octave higher

Student

Use the middle finger of each hand
RH = upstems LH = downstems

Duet

Rhythm Pattern Chant
Du Du Du Du
Du Du Du

S² S¹

Poor Blind Mice

Track 20

Rhythm Pattern Chant
Du Du Du Du
Du Du Du

S² S¹

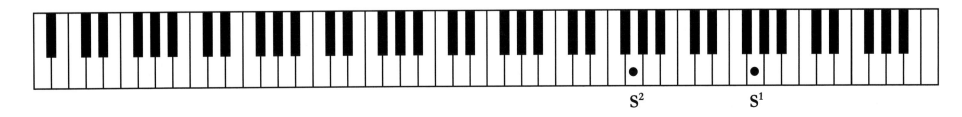

S² S¹

Fireflies

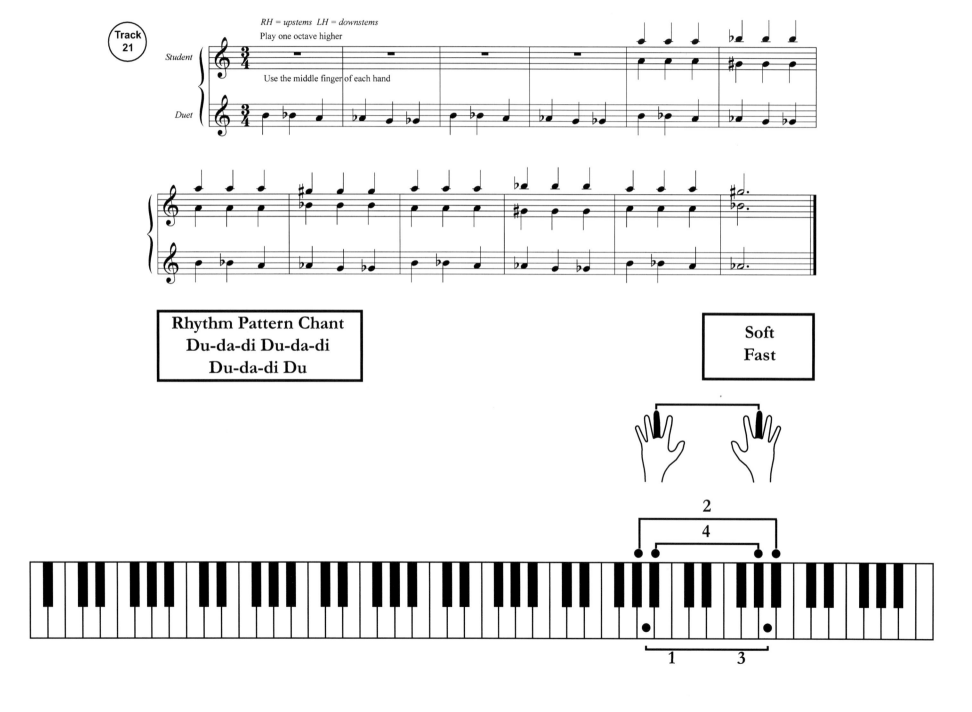

The Buzz Saw

Use the middle fingers and pointer fingers throughout

Rhythm Pattern Chant
Du-da-di Du-da-di Du-da-di Du

Loud
A little fast

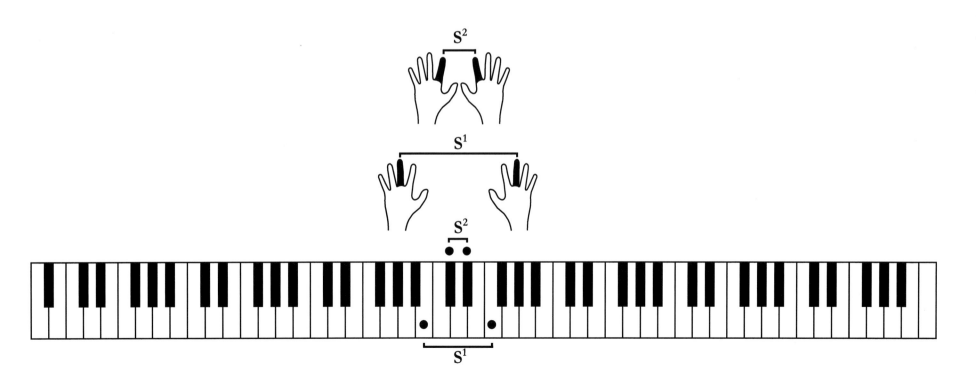

The Mosquito

RH = upstems   LH = downstems
Use the middle finger of each hand

Rhythm Pattern Chant
Du-da-di Du-da-di Du-da-di Du

Medium loud
Fast

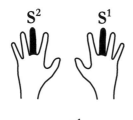

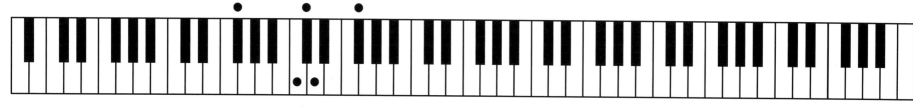

Jolly Old St. Nicholas

Track 24

Rhythm Pattern Chant
Du Du Du Du
Du Du Du

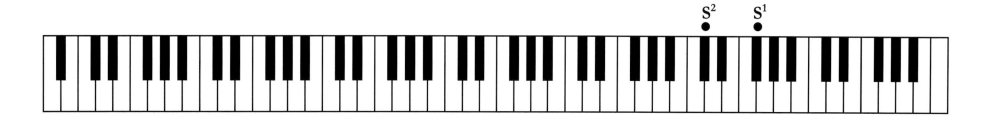

Bluesy Blues

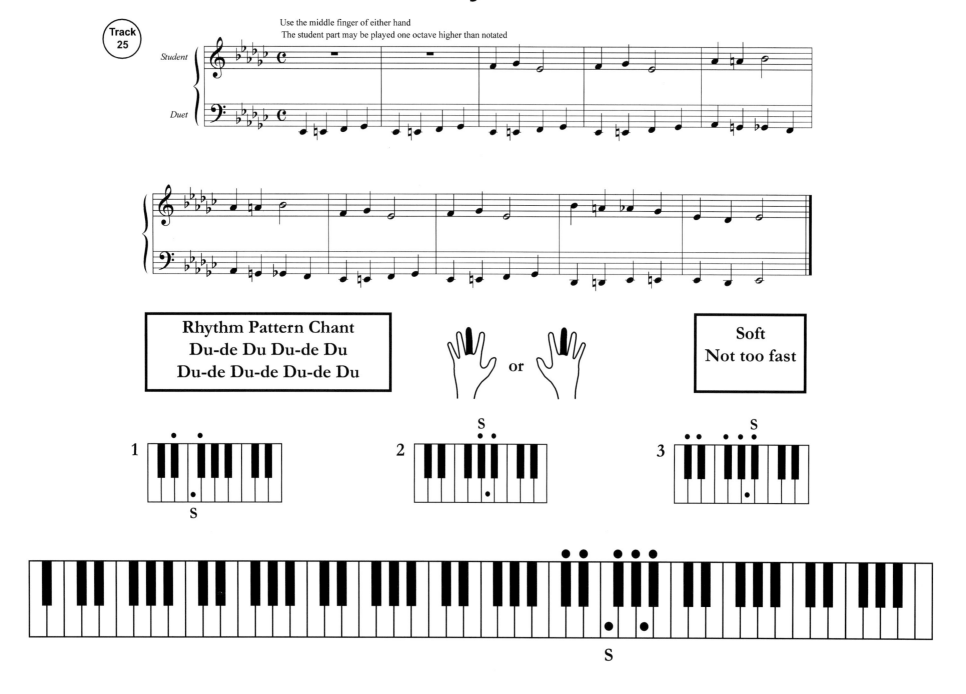

Pop Goes the Weasel

Track 26

Rhythm Pattern Chant
Du Du Du Du

Giant Foot Steps

Use the middle finger of each hand
RH = upstems LH = downstems

Rhythm Pattern Chant
Du-de Du-de Du-de Du-de
Du-de Du-de Du-de Du

Loud
Slow

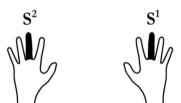

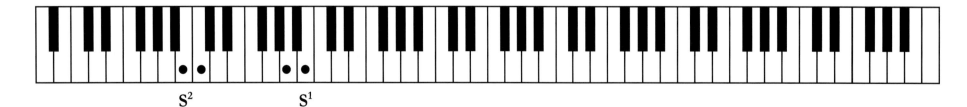

The Pilgrims

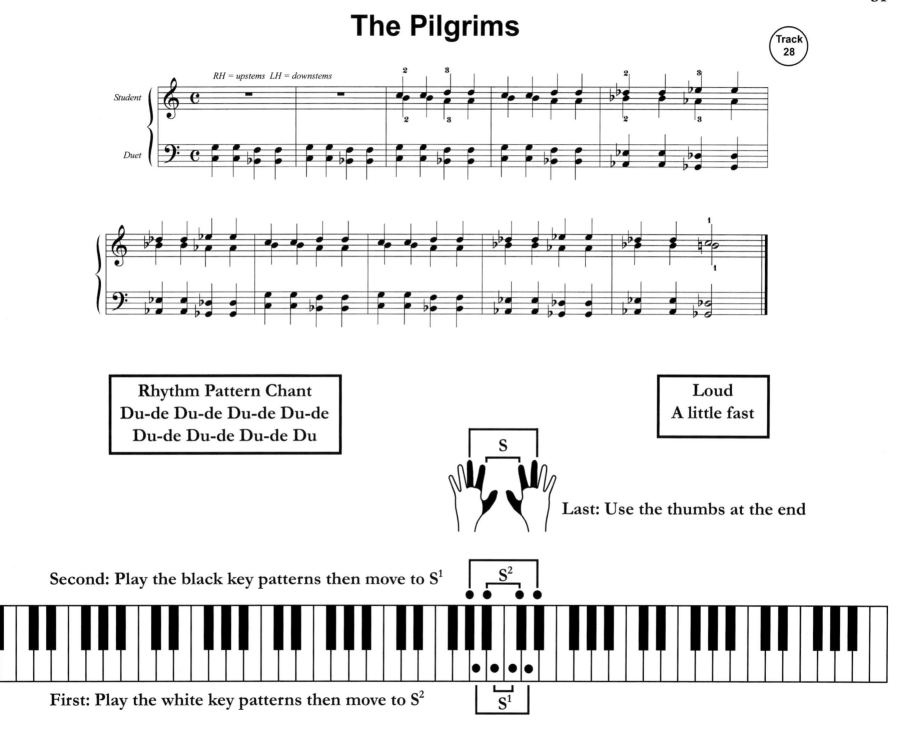

Rhythm Pattern Chant
Du-de Du-de Du-de Du-de
Du-de Du-de Du-de Du

Loud
A little fast

Last: Use the thumbs at the end

Second: Play the black key patterns then move to S¹

First: Play the white key patterns then move to S²

The Low Down Boogie

Track 29

RH = upstems LH = downstems

Rhythm Pattern Chant Du-de Du-de Du-de Du-de Du-de Du-de Du Du		A little loud Not too slow

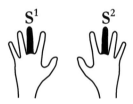

1

2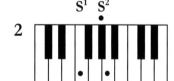

3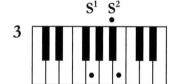

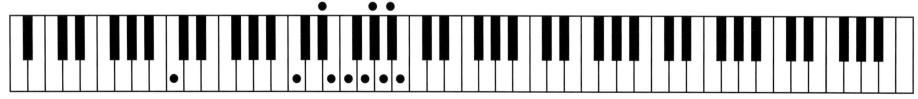

S

The Mulberry Bush

Track 30

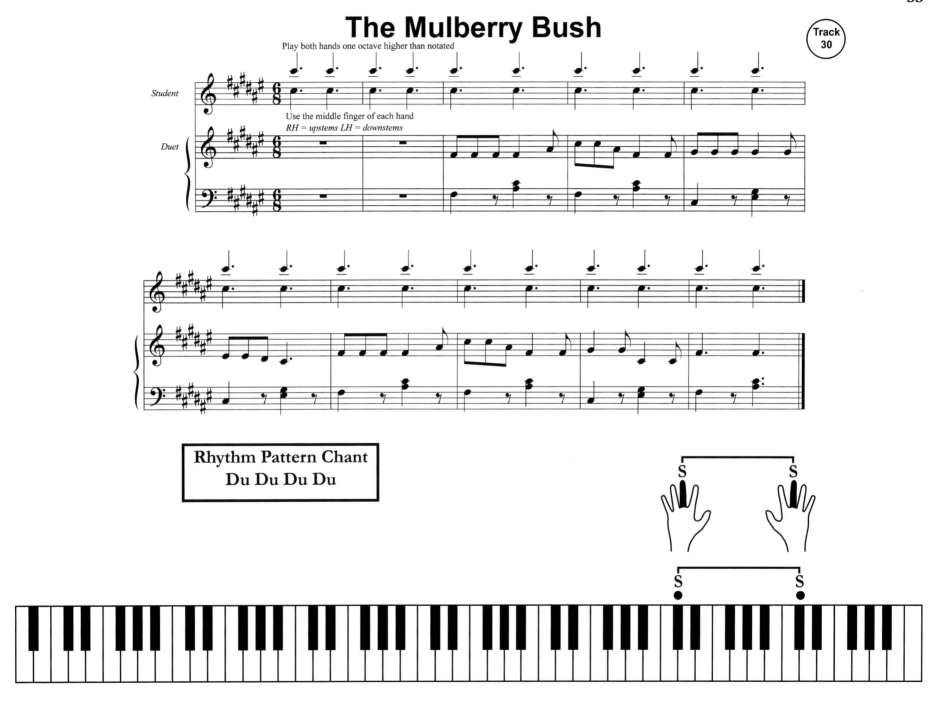

Flint Street Boogie

Track 31

Rhythm Pattern Chant
Du-de Du Du-de Du
Du-de Du-de Du-de Du
Du-de Du-de Du Du

A little loud
Slow

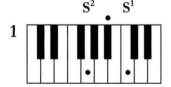

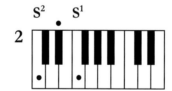

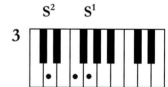

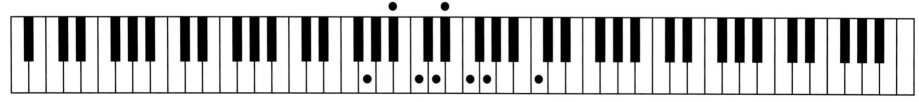

_____

Name of Piece

Circle one from each group

1. Du-de   Du-da-di

2. Soft   Loud

3. Fast   Slow

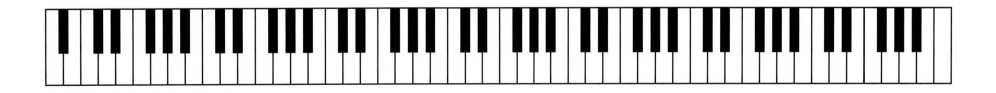

Descriptions of the Keyboard Pieces

Page 1 **"Chocolate Chip Cookies"**

Dynamics:	A little soft
Tempo:	Not too slow
Meter:	Duple
Piano Keys Used:	Four black keys
Keyboard Register:	Treble
Hands:	Left hand alone
Technique:	Arm movement
Duet Part:	Young children can play this

Page 2 **"The Big Black Bear"**

Dynamics:	Loud
Tempo:	Slow
Meter:	Triple
Piano Keys Used:	Sets of black keys
Keyboard Register:	Low to middle
Hands:	Left hand only
Technique:	Arm movement

Page 3 **"Creepy Crawly"**

Dynamics:	Soft
Tempo:	Slow
Meter:	Triple
Piano Keys Used:	A set of three black keys and three white keys
Keyboard Register:	Middle
Hands:	Two hands play separately
Technique:	Arm movement

Page 4 **"Yankee Doodle"**

Dynamics:	Soft
Tempo:	A little fast
Meter:	Duple
Piano Keys Used:	One white and one black key (drum sound)
Keyboard Register:	Low
Hands:	Two hands play together on macrobeats
Technique:	Hands together arm movement
Duet Part:	Young children can play this using any fingers

Page 5 **"The Flower Garden"**

Dynamics:	Soft
Tempo:	Slow
Meter:	Triple
Piano Keys Used:	White keys (notes from a C Major triad)
Keyboard Register:	Bass
Hands:	Two hands play together
Technique:	Arm movement
Duet Part:	Played by the teacher

Page 6 **"Waddling Ducks"**

Dynamics:	Loud
Tempo:	Slow
Meter:	Duple
Piano Keys Used:	Alternating black and white keys
Keyboard Register:	Bass
Hands:	Two hands play separately
Technique:	Arm movement with the middle finger
Duet Part:	Young children can play this using any fingers

Page 7 **"The Parachute. The Diver."**

Dynamics:	"The Parachute" is loud, "The Diver" is soft
Tempo:	"The Parachute" is slow, "The Diver" is fast
Meter:	Triple
Piano Keys Used:	Repeating black keys
Keyboard Register:	Whole keyboard
Hands:	Right hand alone
Technique:	Arm movement with one finger

Page 9 **"Pepperoni Macaroni"**

Dynamics:	A little loud
Tempo:	A little fast
Meter:	Triple
Piano Keys Used:	White key 5ths
Keyboard Register:	Bass
Hands:	Two hands play together
Technique:	Arm movement
Duet Part:	Played by the teacher

Page 10   "Valentine Box"

Dynamics:	Soft
Tempo:	Not too slow
Meter:	Duple
Piano Keys Used:	White keys
Keyboard Register:	High
Hands:	One hand alone
Technique:	Arm movement
Duet Part:	Played by the teacher with damper pedal

Page 11   "Sinking"

Dynamics:	A little soft
Tempo:	A little fast
Meter:	Triple
Piano Keys Used:	Chromatic
Keyboard Register:	Treble to low
Hands:	Two hands play separately
Technique:	Arm movement and changing register
Duet Part:	Young children can play this

Page 12   "Ring Around the Rosy"

Meter:	Duple
Piano Keys Used:	Alternating black keys
Keyboard Register:	Low
Hands:	Two hands play separately on microbeats (DO-SO sound)
Technique:	Alternating arm movement using the middle fingers
	Transposition to a new keyality
Duet Part:	Young children can play this using any fingers

Page 13   "Dance of the Penguins"

Dynamics:	A little loud
Tempo:	Slow
Meter:	Triple
Piano Keys Used:	Three pair of 2nds
Keyboard Register:	Middle
Hands:	Two hands alternate playing
Technique:	Alternating arm movement
Duet Part:	Played by the teacher

Page 15   "Are You Sleeping"

Meter:	Duple
Piano Keys Used:	Two white keys (DO-SO sound)
Keyboard Register:	High
Hands:	Two hands play separately on microbeats
Technique:	Alternating arm movement using the middle fingers
Duet Part:	Played by the teacher
	Young children can play the bass clef duet part

Page 16   "The Ghost"

Dynamics:	Not too soft
Tempo:	Slow
Meter:	Duple
Piano Keys Used:	Chromatic around two black keys
Keyboard Register:	Bass
Hands:	Left hand alone
Technique:	Arm movement using the middle finger
Duet Part:	Young children can play this

Page 17   "Splashing in Puddles"

Dynamics:	A little loud
Tempo:	A little slow
Meter:	Triple
Piano Keys Used:	White and black keys around bass C
Keyboard Register:	Bass
Hands:	Two hands play together
Technique:	Hands together arm movement
Duet Part:	Played by the teacher

Page 18   "Mary Had a Little Lamb"

Meter:	Duple
Piano Keys Used:	Two sets of two black keys
Keyboard Register:	High
Hands:	Two hands and two fingers play together on microbeats
Technique:	Hands together movement in contrary motion
Duet Part:	Played by the teacher
	Young children can play the melody or the bass clef duet part

Page 19   "Bears' Waltz"

Dynamics:	Loud
Tempo:	Slow
Meter:	Triple
Piano Keys Used:	White keys and three black keys
Keyboard Register:	Low and middle
Hands:	Alternating hands
Technique:	Arm movement
Duet Part:	Young children can play this

Page 20   "Jazzy Crocodile"

Dynamics:	A littl loud
Tempo:	A little fast
Meter:	Duple
Piano Keys Used:	Black keys and one white key
Keyboard Register:	Treble
Hands:	Alternating hands using only middle fingers
Technique:	Arm movement
Duet Part:	Played by the teacher

Page 22   "Three Blind Mice"

Meter:	Triple
Piano Keys Used:	Two black keys (SO-DO sound)
Keyboard Register:	High
Hands:	Two hands play separately on macrobeats
Technique:	Alternating arm movement using the middle fingers
Duet Part:	Played by the teacher
	Young children can play the bass clef duet part

Page 23   "Poor Blind Mice"

Meter:	Triple
Piano Keys Used:	Octave G (MI-MI sound)
Keyboard Register:	High
Hands:	Two hands play separately on macrobeats
Technique:	Alternating arm movement using the middle fingers
Duet Part:	Played by the teacher
	Young children can play the bass clef duet part

Page 24   "Fireflies"

Dynamics:	Soft
Tempo:	Fast
Meter:	Triple
Piano Keys Used:	White and black key chromatics
Keyboard Register:	High
Hands:	Two hands play together
Technique:	Arm movement
Duet Part:	Young children can play this

Page 25   "The Buzz Saw"

Dynamics:	Loud
Tempo:	A little fast
Meter:	Triple
Piano Keys Used:	A set of two black keys and two white keys
Keyboard Register:	Middle
Hands:	Two hands play together
	Fingers two and three
Technique:	Arm movement

Page 26   "The Mosquito"

Dynamics:	Medium loud
Tempo:	Fast
Meter:	Triple
Piano Keys Used:	Chromatics
Keyboard Register:	Bass
Hands:	Two hands play separately
Technique:	Arm movement

Page 27   "Jolly Old St. Nicholas"

Meter:	Duple
Piano Keys Used:	Two black keys (DO-SO sound)
Keyboard Register:	High
Hands:	Two hands play separately on macrobeats
Technique:	Alternating arm movement using the middle fingers
Duet Part:	Played by the teacher
	Young children can play the melody using any fingers

Page 28 **"Bluesy Blues"**
Dynamics:	Soft
Tempo:	Not too fast
Meter:	Duple
Piano Keys Used:	Seven piano keys
Keyboard Register:	High
Hands:	Either hand plays alone
Technique:	Arm movement using the middle finger
Duet Part:	Played by the teacher

Page 29 **"Pop Goes the Weasel"**
Meter:	Triple
Piano Keys Used:	Octave white keys (DO-DO sound)
Keyboard Register:	High
Hands:	Two hands play separately on macrobeats
Technique:	Alternating arm movement using the middle fingers
Duet Part:	Played by the teacher
	Young children can play the bass clef duet part

Page 30 **"Giant Foot Steps"**
Dynamics:	Loud
Tempo:	Slow
Meter:	Duple
Piano Keys Used:	White keys
Keyboard Register:	Low
Hands:	Two hands play separately and together
Technique:	Arm movement

Page 31 **"The Pilgrims"**
Dynamics:	Loud
Tempo:	A little fast
Meter:	Duple
Piano Keys Used:	Eight piano keys
Keyboard Register:	Treble
Hands:	Two hands play together using adjacent fingers
Technique:	Moving between white keys and black keys

Page 32 **"The Low Down Boogie"**
Dynamics:	A little loud
Tempo:	Not too slow
Meter:	Duple
Piano Keys Used:	Ten piano keys (blues sound and form)
Keyboard Register:	Bass
Hands:	Two hands play separately
Technique:	Arm movement using the middle fingers and change of playing location

Page 33 **"The Mulberry Bush"**
Meter:	Triple
Piano Keys Used:	Octave C sharps (SO sound))
Keyboard Register:	High
Hands:	Two hands play together on macrobeats
Technique:	Hands together arm movement using the middle fingers
Duet Part:	Played by the teacher
	Young children can play the bass clef duet part if arranged in using only I and V roots

Page 34 **"Flint Street Boogie"**
Dynamics:	A little loud
Tempo:	Slow
Meter:	Duple
Piano Keys Used:	Eight piano keys (blues sound and form)
Keyboard Register:	Middle
Hands:	Two hands play separately
Technique:	Arm movement using middle fingers and change of playing location

Music Moves for Piano is the first piano method of its kind. It applies Edwin E. Gordon's Music Learning Theory to the teaching of piano. When music is taught as an aural art, lessons build a foundation for lifelong musical enjoyment and understanding. With guidance, "sound to notation" leads to fluent music performance, reading, and writing. Following are some of the major concepts of this approach:

- Rhythm is based on body movement: Feel the pulse and meter then chant rhythm patterns. Move in both a continuous fluid way and a rounded, pulsating way.
- Tonal audiation is developed by singing. Singing songs and tonal patterns develops pitch sensitivity, singing in tune, and a "listening" ear.
- Music pattern vocabularies are acquired and applied to listening and performing
- Various elements of music, such as rhythm, meter, pulse, tonality, harmony, style, and form, are studied.
- Creativity is fostered by using different elements of music, such as rhythm, pitch, harmony, and form to create something new.
- Improvisation activities apply everything a student learns. Use familiar patterns from folk songs, transpose, change tonality and meter, create variations and medleys, and create melodic, harmonic, and rhythmic variations.
- Perform with technical freedom. Students learn how to use the playing apparatus from the beginning of lessons.

Marilyn Lowe, who has taught piano for more than 40 years, has used her experiences and knowledge to create a non-traditional piano method based on Edwin E. Gordon's theories of audiation. Other influences include the techniques and theories of Carl Orff, Shinichi Suzuki, Emile Jaques-Dalcroze, Zoltan Kodaly, and Dorothy Taubman. Lowe has been using this approach successfully with her students for more than 20 years. Her academic credits include degrees in liberal arts and piano from Knox College in Galesburg, Illinois, and a master's degree in piano from Indiana University in Bloomington. Lowe completed additional graduate study in organ and music theory at Indiana University. She would like to express appreciation to her former music teachers: Nadia Boulanger, Murray Baylor, Walter Robert, and Menahem Pressler.

Edwin E. Gordon is known throughout the world as a preeminent researcher, teacher, author, editor, and lecturer in the field of music education. In addition to advising doctoral candidates in music education, Gordon has devoted many years to teaching music to preschool-aged children. Through extensive research, Gordon has made major contributions to the field of music education in such areas as the study of music aptitudes, stages and types of audiation, music learning theory, and rhythm in movement and music.

Credits

Music Engraver: Doug Lowe
    Assistants: Louis Claussen
                  William Chiles
Layout/Design: Mary E. Geise
Cover Designs:
    William Chiles
    Brad Scott
    Lori Tack
Editor: Amber Stenger
Consultant: Jennifer Lowe
Original Music/Arrangements:
    Andrea Apostoli
    Michael Brill
    Marilyn Lowe
    Francesca Tortora
Performers:
    Marilyn Lowe, Piano
    John H. Morton, Vocal
    Jerry Pollock, Vocal
    Tina Sibley, Vocal
    Betty Warren, Vocal
    Julie Wilkins, Vocal
Recording Studio:
    Music Precedent Ltd.
Engineer: John H. Morton